Active Learning
Curriculum for Excellence

S1 ENGLISH
Activity Workbook

David Cockburn

CONTENTS

TOOLS FOR LISTENING AND TALKING

ANSWERS

ABOUT THE ACTIVE LEARNING SERIES

Leckie & Leckie's Active Learning series has been developed specifically to help teachers, students and parents implement the Curriculum for Excellence Initiative as effectively as possible. Each book is subject-based, written for a specific year group and follows the Outcomes and Experiences at a level appropriate for that year group. Activity for every subject, both a Course Notes book and an Activity Workbook have been published.

These highly innovative books complement existing class textbooks. They address the Curriculum for Excellence Initiative in a thoroughly practical way that makes learning both engaging and fun! A summary of each topic is included before going on to focus on ideas for activities and rich tasks, bringing the topic to life. In line with the principles and philosophies of Curriculum for Excellence, every Course Notes book provides creative ideas for making cross-disciplinary links with other classroom subjects, and, crucially, illustrates the relevance of each topic to everyday life.

The Activity Workbooks present yet more ideas for activities and offer easy to implement suggestions for:

- inter-disciplinary project work,
- topic revision questions,
- an assessment checklist and
- a four capacities mind map.

This ground-breaking new series provides you with a toolkit of ideas, subject links and activities for you to use in the classroom and/or at home.

Leckie & Leckie's Active Learning series - bringing Curriculum for Excellence to life.

LAYOUT OF YOUR ACTIVITY WORKBOOK

This Activity Workbook follows the structure of the accompanying Course Notes book, and has the same chapter headings.

Each chapter of the Activity Workbook contains several double page spreads:

- The first double page spread contains revision questions across all the topics included in the corresponding Course Notes chapter.
- The next double page spread contains an idea for a multi-disciplinary project, and suggestions for individual, paired and group activities.
- The final double page spread in each Activity Workbook chapter includes an assessment checklist and a Four Capacities Mind Map.

TOOLS FOR WRITING

QUESTIONS

QUICK QUESTIONS

1. Put the following words into meaningful sentences. Make sure that capital letters are in all the right places.

   (a) scotland the city of is edinburgh capital

   ....

   ....

   (b) organisation a is facebook networking

   ....

   ....

   (c) bolognese italian my is favourite meal spaghetti

   ....

   ....

2. Underline the nouns in the following paragraph, from Boy: *Tales of Childhood*, by Roald Dahl.

   My father, Harald Dahl, was a Norwegian who came from a small town near Oslo, called Sarpsborg. His own father, my grandfather, was a fairly prosperous merchant who owned a store on Sarpsborg and traded in just about everything from cheese to chicken-wire.

3. Identify all the abstract nouns in the following sentences.
   (a) The girl was filled with joy when she heard she had passed her exams.
   (b) The trouble with that boy is that his head is full of nonsense.
   (c) Amazement was written over her entire face.

4. Underline the verbs in the following sentences.

   (a) The train from Inverness will arrive at Platform 10.
   (b) All passengers must have their boarding passes ready.
   (c) By the time we get to Ullapool it will be too late to catch the ferry.

5. Identify the verbs in the following sentences. Once you have done that, identify the tenses used. The first one has been done for you.
   (a) The boy is eating the apple.

VERB	TENSE
is eating	Continuous present tense

   (b) The young man was waiting for his wife to come home from work.

   ....

   ....

   (c) The girl hadn't seen last night's *Coronation Street.*

   ....

   ....

   (d) The new swimming pool will be open in time for the summer holidays.

   ....

   ....

6. Identify the adjectives in the following sentences.
   (a) The sea today is a beautiful shade of sapphire blue.
   (b) That banana is an odd shape.

(c) The shopping centre was empty yesterday morning.

(d) I live in the most central town in bonnie Scotland.

. Make sense of the following sentences by inserting punctuation. You need to insert capital letters in the appropriate places.

(a) michael bought all his tools from the do it yourself shop

....

....

(b) the train for dingwall has been delayed there are leaves on the line

....

....

(c) andrew went to the odeon in dunfermline yesterday he saw the latest blockbuster

....

....

MAKES YOU THINK

1. Put the following words into meaningful sentences. Make sure that capital letters are in all the right places.

(a) millionth language reached the its english word has now

....

....

(b) an boxes with all in fill please asterisk marked

....

....

(c) address provided space in the your to need you enter

....

....

2. Underline the nouns in the following paragraphs, from *Knots and Crosses*, by Ian Rankin.

The station was old, its floor dark and marbled. It had about it the fading grandeur of a dead aristocracy. It had character. Rebus waved to the duty sergeant, who was tearing old pictures from the noticeboard and pinning up new ones in their place. He climbed the great curving staircase to his office. Campbell was just leaving.

3. Make the following words into abstract nouns.

(a) rapid ....

(b) ideal ....

(c) friend ....

4. Underline the verbs in the following paragraphs from *Stone Cold*, by Robert Swindells.

You can call me Link. It's not my name, but it's what I say when anybody asks, which isn't often. I'm invisible, see? One of the invisible people. Right now, I'm sitting in a doorway watching the passers-by. They avoid looking at me. They're afraid that I want something they've got, and they're right.

5. Here is a set of instructions about how to care for a new duvet. Read the instructions carefully and then identify all the verbs. Once you have done that, identify the tenses used.

   This product has been roll packed for convenience. To restore fullness, you should shake well after opening. Washing in a launderette machine is recommended. Duvets should be thoroughly dried and aired before use.

....

....

....

....

....

6. Which of the following words are adjectives?

   (a) pity (b) leave

   (c) ugly (d) quickly

   (e) satisfactory (f) furious

   (g) silent

....

....

....

   Make up sentences using the words you identified as adjectives.

....

....

....

....

7. Make sense of the following sentences by inserting punctuation. You need to insert capital letters in the appropriate places.

   From *Stone Cold*, by Robert Swindells

   born march 20th 1977 in bradford Yorkshire to mr and mrs x we were a family you know as happy as most till dad ran off with a receptionist in 1991 when i was fourteen and at the local comp this mucked up my school work for quite a while but thats not why i ended up like this no vincents to blame for that good old vince mums boyfriend

CHALLENGERS

1. Put the following words into meaningful sentences. Make sure that capital letters are in all the right places.

   (a) grandfather my sixty-four today been alive if he hundred had been and would have one years old

....

....

....

   (b) twenty-one would been my hundred have one and father

....

....

....

....

2. Work out at *least six ways*, with examples for each, by which abstract nouns are formed. Here are two ways:

   By adding –ness to the adjective: for example, happy + ness = happiness.

   By adding –hood to a noun: for example, boy + hood = boyhood.

....

....

....

....

....

3. Underline the verbs in the following paragraphs, from *'Pride and Prejudice'*, by Jane Austen.

   "My dear Mr Bennet," said his lady to him one day, "have you heard that Netherfield Park is let at last?"

   Mr Bennet replied that he had not.

   "But it is," returned she; "for Mrs Long has just been there, and she told me all about it."

   Mr Bennet made no answer.

   "Do not you want to know who has taken it?" cried his wife impatiently.

   "You want to tell me, and I have no objection to hearing it."

   This was invitation enough.

4. Read carefully the following extract, taken from an article by Melanie Reid about Children's television. She is presenting what she sees as the real purpose behind the growth in children's television. Once again, identify the verbs, and once you have done that, indicate the tenses used.

   But there is another purpose, of course. The real reason behind the explosion in children's TV is the fact that it makes a lot of people very, very rich. In 1984 the US deregulated children's TV, which meant characters such as the Power Rangers and the Teenage Mutant Ninja Turtles could be advertised in the commercial breaks of the show. By the end of the 1980s, children's TV had become a huge global money-spinner, firmly in the grip of the marketing men.

....

....

....

....

....

....

....

....

....

....

....

5. Make sense of the following sentences by inserting punctuation. You need to insert capital letters in the appropriate places. This extract is from *The Prime of Miss Jean Brodie*, by Muriel Spark

   whoever has opened the window has opened it too wide said miss brodie six inches is perfectly adequate more is vulgar one should have an innate sense of these things we ought to be doing history at the moment according to the timetable get out your history books and prop them up in your hands i shall tell you a little more about italy here is a picture of dante meeting beatrice it is pronounced beatrichay in italian which makes the name very beautiful on the ponte vecchio he fell in love with her at that moment mary sit up and don't slouch

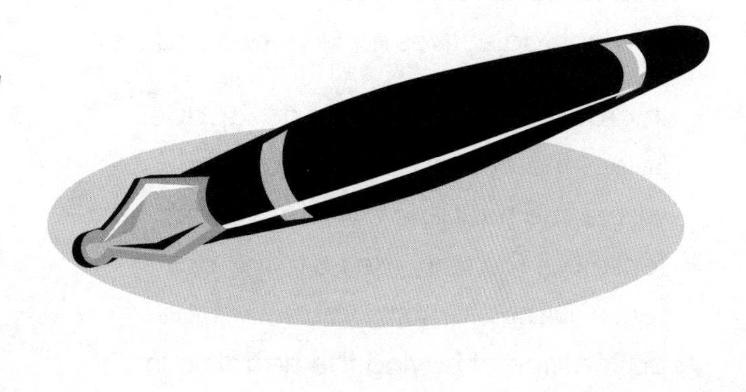

TOOLS FOR WRITING

MAKE THE LINK

INTERDISCIPLINARY PROJECT

1. In groups, plan the launch of a brand new chocolate. The chocolates are to be aimed at the top end of the market and are priced at £10 per box. This project can involve the departments of **craft and design**, **art and design**, **business**, **geography** and **modern languages** as well as **English**.

   (a) Design the box to make it appeal to wealthy chocolate lovers. It has to be striking yet stylish, using colour to draw attention to it, making it compete with its rivals on the shelves of specialist chocolate shops.
   (b) Design the poster that is to launch the product.
   (c) Write a magazine advert for the chocolates.
   (d) Think of two other countries to sell the chocolates to. Design an advert for each of these two countries, using your foreign language skills if necessary.

> **TOP TIP**
> As well as design, you have to think of the language (especially the advertising copy) that will help to sell the product.

2. In groups, collect ten adverts, all of which use adjectives and try to work out in your discussions how these adjectives are being used – what purpose do they serve? Do they help to state facts, or are they expressing the manufacturers' opinions?
   If, for example, some brand of chocolate is the tastiest or, crumbliest ask yourself what that means – these adjectives have to do with comparisons, so what exactly is the tastiest, crumbliest chocolate being compared with? If a produce is advertised as 'probably the best', what is the effect on meaning of the word 'probably'?
   Report back to the rest of the class your group's thoughts about these adverts and the ways in which adjectives have been used.

3. In groups, read through a newspaper. Select the best example of a story where the headline is in the present tense but the story itself is in the past tense. Discuss among yourselves the advantage of having the headline in the present tense.
   Still in your groups, change the story itself into the present tense, solving any problems as you go along.

QUICK TASKS

1. Think of something that has happened recently to you. In about 150 words, write the opening of the story using only the present tense.

....

....

....

....

....

....

2. Now write the remainder of the same story in the past tense.

....

....

....

....

....

....

....

....

....

....

....

....

....

....

....

....

....

....

....

....

....

....

MY PROGRESS

MY LEARNING CHECKLIST

1. *I can punctuate different types of sentences correctly.* ○
2. *I can identify nouns, verbs and adjectives in different types of sentences.* ○
3. *I can use past, present and future tense correctly.* ○
4. *I can explain why grammar is important in English and other languages.* ○
5. *I have explored different spelling strategies and improved my spelling by using at least one of these strategies.* ○
6. *I have explored the way English is used in different texts, e.g. newspapers and adverts.* ○

1. Learning about grammar will help me improve my writing skills by:

....

....

2. Grammar is important in every day life because:

....

....

FOUR CAPACITIES MIND MAP

Studying grammar will help me to become a successful learner by:

1. *Making my written communication clearer.*

2.

3.

4.

5.

6.

CREATING TEXTS

QUESTIONS

QUICK QUESTIONS

1. What are the four aspects of writing?

....

....

....

....

2. Write a sentence about each of the four aspects of writing in turn, giving in your own words an explanation of each aspect.

....

....

....

....

....

MAKES YOU THINK

1. Rewrite the following sentences using text language where possible.
   (a) What are you doing after school?

....

   (b) Do you want to see a movie tomorrow night?

....

   (c) My mum's grounded me until Monday. I can't believe it.

....

2. (a) The following text is from the opening chapter of *Pennington's Seventeenth Summer* by K.M.Peyton. It clearly was written some time ago – in the early 1970s – and some of the vocabulary, sentence structures, and even ideas seem out-of-date to a modern reader.

Rewrite the episode, updating it so that it makes sense and appeals to someone living in the 21st Century.

Penn read slowly down his report. Apart from games – 'Excellent' – the remarks were the usual, brief and unenthusiastic: 'Poor', 'Fair', 'Could do better'. Under Mathematics it said, 'Idle and destructive in class, in spite of innate ability', and under the heading 'Extras: Music' a crabbed hand had written angrily, 'May God forgive this boy for so abusing so unusual a talent.' Penn pondered this remark, scowling. Then he yawned, and passed the document on to his friend, Bates.

Bates read it and said, 'Only Dotty Crocker makes any effort at all. He gave you a good one last term. How did it go?'
"This boy plays the piano as befits the captain of the first eleven".'
'Yes. That was good.'
'A plus,' Penn agreed.
'What's Soggy said?'
Penn turned the report over to 'Character and Obedience'.
"Unsatisfactory in the extreme. It is imperative that Pennington cultivates a sense of responsibility in keeping with his position in the school",' he read.
'Old enough to have more sense,' Bates translated.
'Old enough to leave,' Penn said heavily.

TOP TIP
Remember you can write essay plans for essays in other subjects such as history.

(b) Think about the story you have written so far. Going by the clues in the original story, what do you think might happen next to Pennington? Once you've decided, write the next part of the story.

CHALLENGERS

1. Why do you think writing skills are important?

2. What kinds of things can you do to improve your writing skills?

3. Why is it important to plan an essay or an article?

MAKE THE LINK

INTERDISCIPLINARY PROJECT

In groups, you are going to write an article for your school newspaper on what life was like in a previous decade. You can choose the 1960s, the 1970s or the 1980s – decide as a group which decade you prefer. For this project, you may like to involve the **History** and **ICT** departments as well as the **English** department.

Next decide how to carry out your research. Do any of you know someone who lived through the decade you have chosen? Grandparents, parents, uncles, aunts, neighbours? If so, those team members should try to arrange an interview with that person. Take notes on your discussion, so that you can report back to the rest of the group. Ask questions about what life was like – what was their home life like, what was their social life like, which hobbies were popular, what types of food were popular, and so on. What were your interviewee's hopes and expectations? How does the person see the 21st century – have things turned out as he or she expected?

Other team members should carry out some internet research about the decade you are writing about. What were the major events of that decade? What were music, television and fashion like? Your ICT teacher will be able to help you with internet research skills. Again, make notes on your research so that you can report back to the rest of the team.
You may also like to ask your History teacher for help with this project. Can he or she recommend any books or articles about your chosen decade? What does he or she think were the major events of that decade?

Finally, write up your newspaper article, keeping in mind the four aspects of writing: purpose, structure, reader and register. Make your opening paragraph as interesting and lively as possible in order to engage your readers' interest.

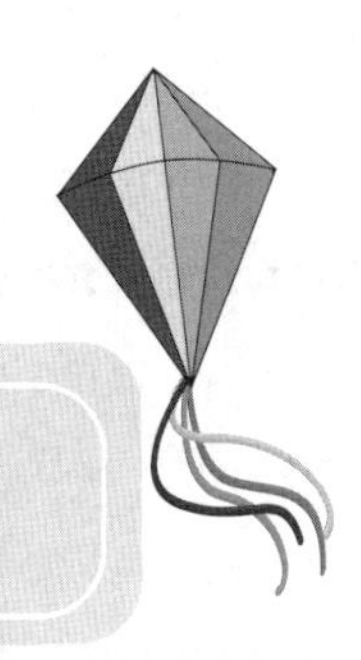

BE ACTIVE

QUICK TASKS

1. Keep a diary for a week. It should record the things you have done, any visits you have made or any events you have attended. But more than that, the diary should also record how you felt about things, say something about your relationships with other people – parents, teachers, friends. In other words, the diary isn't just a list of all that you have done, it should also reflect on your experiences and be personal.

2. Working in pairs, read the following article from *The Sun* newspaper about the millionth word to join the English language.

U.S. BOFFINS DETERMINE DICTIONARY MILESTONE

The millionth word to join the English language is...

THE millionth word to be commonly used in the English language has just been announced.

It should be a landmark moment. But the word does not match up to this exciting event. In fact, many Brits could use a few fruity ones to describe it!

The Global Language Monitor, based in Texas, searches the internet to track the frequency of words and phrases.

When a new one appears more than 25,000 times, they count it. And at 10.22am yesterday the millionth word clocked in. Here is the countdown to the language milestone and, below, others which nearly made the list.

Other recent contenders

MOBAMA: Relating to fashion sense of US First Lady Michelle Obama.

CHICONOMICS: The ability to maintain one's fashion sense, such as shopping at Primark, in the middle of the current financial crisis.

E-VAMPIRES: Appliances on stand-by mode, which still use electricity while they "sleep".

WONDERSTAR: As in Susan Boyle, an overnight sensation exceeding all reasonable expectations.

BANGSTERS: Loan sharks, from the words bankers and gangsters.

PHELPSIAN: The achievements of multiple gold medal winner Michael Phelps at the Beijing Olympics.

999,990 **SHOVEL READY:** Projects which are ready to begin immediately upon the release of government stimulus funds.

999,991 **SEXTING:** Sending an email or text with sexual content.

999,992 **GREENWASHING:** Re-branding an old, often inferior product as environmentally friendly.

999,993 **OCTOMOM:** Media phenomenon relating to the American mother of octuplets, Nadya Suleman.

999,994 **SLOW FOOD:** Food other than the fast-food variety.

999,995 **CARBON NEUTRAL:** The balance achieved by offsetting the use of carbon-producing fossil fuels by the planting of CO_2-absorbing plants or trees.

999,996 **CLOUD COMPUTING:** The cloud has been technical jargon for the internet for many years. It is now passing into more general usage.

999,997 **SLUMDOG:** A formerly disparaging, now often endearing, description of those residing in the slums of India. Popularised by the Oscar-winning movie Slumdog Millionaire.

999,998 **NOOB** (that's N Zero Zero B): From the gamer community, a disparaging term for a newcomer joining in an online game.

999,999 **JAI HO!:** The Hindi phrase signifying the joy of victory, used as an exclamation. From movie Slumdog Millionaire.

And here it is – the millionth word you've all been waiting for . . .

1,000,000 **WEB 2.0:** The next generation of web products, coming soon to a browser near you.

Write a report using the information from this article about how new words come into the English language. Between the two of you, decide which notes you need to take for your report; think about what the most important points are, what will be relevant for your article, and about the ways in which new words tend to be formed. Then write the report, using your notes.

3. Working in pairs, write a ghost story for the 21st Century. It has to be set in the country and should be set at night. In your opening paragraphs, try to create an atmosphere that is as eerie as you can, but remember it has to be modern. Maybe it's a lonely, isolated house, surrounded by trees. Use the weather and the moon to help with the atmosphere. Think of the characters involved – you do not want too many, three at the most. One of the characte must believe in ghosts and the second character must not. The third character can be as you please – and they can be all boys, all girls, or a mix. They are all teenagers. Think about why they are there. Where are their parents? What time of year is it? Are they on holiday? Whatever the situation – there are events that take place which are difficult to explain. But the outcome of the story is up to you. Is everything explained to the reader, or is the reader left wondering?

4. Imagine the following situation. You have been staying with your grandmother for the weekend. She lives on her own and is a bit frail, but independent. She adores you and thinks you can do no wrong. She is also a bit naïve, especially where you are concerned. It is in the middle of the summer holidays. You go out on the Saturday evening about 7 p.m. to see one of your friends. You don't come home until late, and you are soaking wet (it hasn't been raining), you are covered in mud, and it looks as though you have hurt your leg – there is blood seeping through the mud. When you appear, your grandmother is visibly upset and worried and asks you what on earth you had been doing.
Relate what happened to you so that she will be convinced that there is nothing to be worrie about, and making yourself out not only to be completely innocent but also to have been a bit of a hero. When you get back home, you tell your best friend what really happened. Pa close attention to register – use vocabulary and sentence structure to suit your two entirely different audiences. Write out both stories.

. Write about a time when an experience you had turned out to be really funny. Maybe it involved your family, or friends or a pet you were given. It could have been a part you had in a play or musical. Maybe it was something like a dreadful holiday that turned out to have a funny side. Whatever you decide to write about, remember to include how you felt at the time or afterwards – this is a personal essay and must include your personal feelings. Remember the four aspects of writing – ***purpose***, ***structure***, ***reader***, ***register***. Once you have decided what you are going to write about, start your plan. Once you are satisfied with your plan, begin the essay. You must include your plan in the final version of your essay.

CREATING TEXTS

MY PROGRESS

MY LEARNING CHECKLIST

1. I understand the four aspects of writing and can use them to write different texts.	◯
2. I can write an essay plan and I intend always to produce one from now onwards.	◯
3. I can make notes and use them to help me write a text.	◯
4. I am developing my own style of writing.	◯
5. I have written at least two different types of essays.	◯

1. Being able to write clearly and well will help me in my everyday life by:

....

....

2. I will continue to improve my writing skills by:

....

....

OUR CAPACITIES MIND MAP

1. *Allowing me to express my own opinions clearly and well.*

2. ....

3. ....

4. ....

5. ....

6. ....

Having good writing skills helps me to become and effective contributor by:

QUESTIONS

QUICK QUESTIONS

1. What does the term 'close reading' mean? Use your own words as far as possible.

....
....
....
....
....
....

2. Why should you develop close reading skills?

....
....
....
....
....
....

3. What is meant by the term 'reading for understanding'?

....
....
....
....
....
....

4. (a) Make a list of ten texts – novels, short stories, poems – that you have really enjoyed reading recently.

....
....
....
....
....
....
....
....
....
....

(b) Now make a list of anything that you read at least once a week – anything from the side of cornflake packets, bus timetables, supermarket promotions, instructions for equipment and television adverts to magazines.

....
....
....
....
....
....
....
....
....

TOP TIP
Reading different types of text will help build your vocabulary as well as your reading skills.

5. Explain in your own words and as clearly as you can the difference between fact and opinion.

....
....
....
....
....
....
....
....
....

. List all the Scots words that you know for rain (including rainy conditions).

. Write out, as clearly as possible, the instructions for:

(a) creating a Facebook profile,

(b) making a mobile phone call,

(c) entering a new number that someone has just given you into your mobile phone.

MAKES YOU THINK

1. Which of the following sentences are facts and which are opinions? In some cases, you may have to use the internet to confirm your answer.

(a) Inverness is a city.

(b) Dundee has the same size of population as Aberdeen.

(c) Glaswegians have more style than people from other cities in Scotland.

(d) Indian food is spicier than Chinese food.

(e) Broccoli is a superfood and is very good for you.

(f) Ben Nevis is the highest mountain in Britain.

(g) Mobile phones have made communication between people much more effective.

(h) Dogs are cleverer than most people realise.

MAKE THE LINK

INTERDISCIPLINARY PROJECT

You as a group have been commissioned to write a short entry for a brand new tourist information pack for visits to the Antonine Wall (the Roman wall that was built in Central Scotland). You may have to consult the internet, your library, and other departments such as **Geography** and **History**. As you write the guide, you should also bear in mind the kind of people who are likely to visit such a place of historical and national interest.

Your entry needs to deal with:

- where and what is the Antonine wall,
- what its purpose was,
- when it was built,
- who built it,
- the best ways to get to it,
- where to stay,
- other attractions in the area,
- any other points that might encourage tourists to visit it.

....

....

....

Now, in the same groups, write another guide for visitors, this time to Rothesay. Again, you may have to consult the internet, your library and other school departments such as **Geography** and **History**. As you write the guide, you should also bear in mind the kind of people who are likely to want to holiday there.

Your entry should deal with:

- the reasons for holidaying in Rothesay,
- its suitability for families,
- how to get there,
- where to stay, especially for families,
- what there is to do there,
- other places of interest on the island,
- other places of interest you can get to from the island,
- any other points that might encourage families to holiday there.

Make an attempt to translate your guide into the language you are studying or other language that you understand.

....

....

QUICK TASKS

. Read the following passage carefully and then answer the questions which follow. It is taken from James Kirkup's book *The Only Child*.

> *If I ran all the way, I could be home in two minutes, and I would arrive at the back door panting and happy. My mother always had dinner ready for me, and it was a sad dinner-time for me when there was no rice pudding, my favourite dish. On cold, winter days we would have our dinner on trays by the fireside, while the wind roared outside and rain lashed the window-panes and the sea boomed beyond the house-yops. They were happy, cosy, intimate meals. It was a great treat to have dinner or tea by the blazing fire, with our feet up on the sparkling brass fender of the white-washed hearth. But it made going back to school even harder. If there was dense fog outside, I would sit by the fire in my slippers until the last possible minute, listening to the glum blasts of the foghorn and the wailing sirens of fogbound ships outside the harbour. Then, with a high-pitched urgency, the school bell would begin to ring, and I would scramble into my coat and cap and outdoor shoes, cover my mouth and nose with my muffler, and dash out into the dead, damp fog.*

(a) Nowadays dinner-time can be either midday or in the evening. Is dinner-time in this passage at midday or in the evening? Give a reason for your answer.
(b) Give two reasons why the author wants to run all the way home.
(c) The author says that the meals were 'happy, cosy, intimate'. How does he make us feel the cosiness?
(d) Was the author happy or not to go back to school? Give a reason for your answer.
(e) Read the passage again carefully. What can you tell about the kind of town the boy lives in? Pick out three words to support your answer.

MY PROGRESS

MY LEARNING CHECKLIST

1. *I can identify at least three different texts that I read in my daily life for information.* ◯
2. *I can tell the difference between fact and opinion.* ◯
3. *I am able to recognise persuasion.* ◯
4. *I have successfully answered questions on a text that I have read closely.* ◯
5. *I can make inferences from texts.* ◯
6. *I have compared at least two pieces of text to find similarities and differences between them.* ◯

1. Close reading skills will help me in my everyday life by:

....

....

2. Reading for understanding is important because:

....

....

OUR CAPACITIES MIND MAP

1. *I can better understand written instructions, which helps me to do things more successfully, e.g. how to use my new camera.*

2. ....

Reading skills help me to develop my confidence because:

3. ....

4. ....

5. ....

6. ....

QUESTIONS

QUICK QUESTIONS

1. (a) Write out the three questions that we should use to analyse a text which we are reading for enjoyment.

....

....

....

....

....

....

(b) What is the point of asking these three questions – what answers are expected?

....

....

....

....

....

....

2. What, in your own words, does **textual analysis** mean?

....

....

....

....

....

....

3. (a) What does **genre** mean?

....

....

....

(b) What does **sub-genre** mean?

....

....

....

4. Identify the genre and sub-genre of the following works.

(a) *Hamlet*, by William Shakespeare

....

....

(b) *Pride and Prejudice*, by Jane Austen

....

....

(c) *Twilight*, by Stephanie Myers

....

....

(d) *2012*, directed by Roland Emmerich

....

....

(e) *Hollyoaks*, Channel 4

....

....

(f) *A Kestrel for a Knave*, by Barry Hines

....

....

(g) *The Amber Spyglass*, by Philip Pullman

....

....

(h) *Kidnapped*, by Robert Louis Stevenson

....

....

(i) *Ten O'Clock News*, BBC 1

....

....

(j) *Tam O'Shanter*, by Robert Burns

....

....

MAKES YOU THINK

1. (a) What is meant by the **structure** of a story?

....

....

(b) Look again at the novel or short story that you are reading in class. How is it structured? To help you answer this question, think about the timescale over which it is written – is it years, months, days, hours? Does it use flashback?

2. What are the advantages of **first-person narration**? Now list any disadvantages.

3. What is meant by 'point of view'?

CHALLENGERS

1. Often plot is driven by characters fighting against the environment. Many disaster movies use this kind of plot. Can you think of any examples of plot where people are pitched against a hostile environment? Think of novels and short stories as well as films.

2. Sometimes plot is driven by the search for an object: *Lord of the Rings*, by J.R.R. Tolkien is a perfect example of that kind of plot. Can you think of any others?

3. Think about the novel or short story or play that you are studying (or have studied) in class. Write down all that makes up the plot. It's difficult, of course, to separate plot from setting and environment, but try to identify all the features of plot and the plot devices that you can.

MAKE THE LINK

INTERDISCIPLINARY PROJECT

Here are the opening paragraphs of Bram Stoker's *Dracula*. It may seem a bit difficult to read at first simply because it was written over a hundred years ago, but it is worth persevering with the passage. The questions should help you understand most of it.

The paragraphs below are narrated by Jonathan Harker as part of his diary (journal). First of all read it carefully.

Jonathan Harker's Journal
(Kept in the shorthand)

> *3 May. Bistritz. – Left Munich at 8.35 p.m. on 1st May, arriving at Vienna early next morning; arrived at 6.46, but train was an hour late. Buda-Pesth seems a wonderful place, from the glimpse which I got of it from the train and the little I could walk through the streets. I feared to go very far from the station, as we had arrived late and would start as near the correct time as possible. The impression I had was that we were leaving the West and entering the East; the most Western of splendid bridges over the Danube, which is here of noble width and depth, took us among the traditions of Turkish rule.*
>
> *We left in pretty good time, and came after nightfall to Klausenburgh. Here I stopped for the night at the Hotel Royale. I had for dinner, or rather supper, a chicken done up some way with red pepper, which was very good but thirsty. (mem., get recipe for Mina.) I asked the waiter, and he said it was called 'paprika hendl,' and that, as it was a national dish, I should be able to get it anywhere along the Carpathians. I found my smattering of German very useful here; indeed, I don't know how I should be able to get on without it.*
>
> *Having some time at my disposal when in London, I had visited the British Museum, and made search among the books and maps in the library regarding Transylvania; it had struck me that some foreknowledge of the country could hardly fail to have some importance in dealing with a noble of that country. I find that the district he named is in the extreme east of the country, just on the borders of three states, Transylvania, Moldavia and Bukovina, in the midst of the Carpathian mountains; one of the wildest and least known portions of Europe. I was not able to light on any map or work giving the exact locality of the Castle Dracula, as there are no maps of this country as yet to compare with our own Ordnance Survey maps; but I found that Bistritz, the post town named by Count Dracula, is a fairly well-known place. I shall enter here some of my notes, as they may refresh my memory when I talk over my travels with Mina.*

a) Your **Geography** teacher may be able to help you answer the following questions.

(1) Castle Dracula is in Transylvania, 'in the midst of the Carpathian mountains'. Using an Atlas or an internet search engine, find out all you can about the Carpathians and where they are located.

....

(2) Next, try finding out all you can about Transylvania. Where is Transylvania?

....

(3) In the first paragraph, Jonathan Harker mentions the Danube: he talks about 'the most Western of bridges over the Danube, which is here of noble width and depth'. What is the Danube?

....

(4) He also refers to 'Buda-Pesth'. Which modern city is he referring to and which river flows through it?

....

(5) He says that 'there are no maps of this country' (Transylvania) 'as yet to compare with our own Ordnance Survey maps'. What is an Ordnance Survey map and why were they first produced? It would help to find out what is meant by the term 'ordnance'.

....

b) For these questions, you may like to ask your **Home Economics** teacher for help:

(1) What is paprika?

....

(2) Where does paprika come from?

....

(3) If 'hendl' is the Austro-Bavarian word for chicken, what dish do you think Harker ate in Hungary on his way to Transylvania?

....

(4) Find out another recipe that uses paprika.

....

c) Now use the reading skills that you have gained in your **English** class.

(1) What evidence is there that this passage uses first-person narration?

....

(2) It is headed 'Jonathan Harker's Journal'. What is a journal?

....

(3) He mentions Mina. Is there anything in the text which makes you think that Mina is someone important to him?

....

(4) Now work in pairs. Going by what is written here, discuss between the two of you what you think is going to happen next in the story.

READING FOR ENJOYMENT

BE ACTIVE

QUICK TASKS

1. In groups, come up with ideas for the production, design, and direction of a film to be made for a new digital Scottish television station. You have total freedom to make the kind of film that you think will be appropriate for the audience watching this new station, which can reach all parts of Scotland. The film can be aimed at a city audience, or it can have a rural setting – aimed at the Highlands, Islands, or the Borders. You can, of course, make it appeal to both the rural and the urban audience tuned in to this channel.

You need to:

- decide on the theme you want to explore in your film;
- decide where it is to be shot, i.e. the setting;
- decide which characters you need – age, gender, type of people involved – people who get on with each other, people who don't;
- decide on the structure of the film – when is it set? Over what period of time does it take place? Does it involve flashback? How long is it to be – a short film or feature length?;

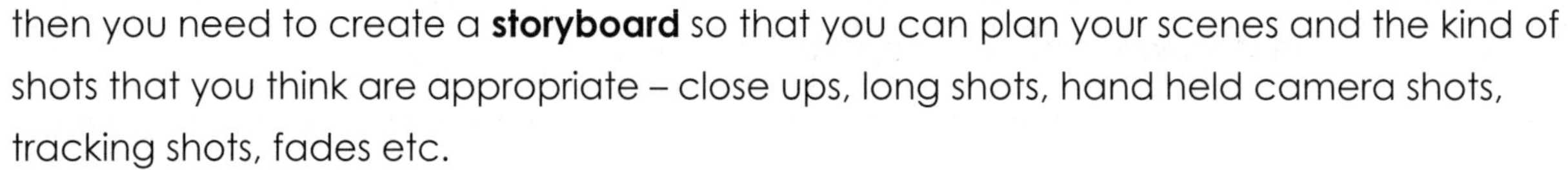

then you need to create a **storyboard** so that you can plan your scenes and the kind of shots that you think are appropriate – close ups, long shots, hand held camera shots, tracking shots, fades etc.

To do all this, you need to think about **theme**, the **storyline**, **setting and characterisation**, and the detailed **techniques** that will help portray your theme. In other words, you need to employ the three questions to ensure a successful film. You may also like to ask the **Art and Design** and **Drama** departments for help.

2. Write the opening paragraphs of your own novel. You are free to choose more or less what you want to write, the method of narration, and the style of writing.

However:

- The novel has to be set in the autumn. You must make it clear – without just stating it – that it is autumn. Think of autumnal weather and colours.
- It has to involve three characters – a father and mother and their son or daughter.
- There has to be the beginnings of conflict – preferably (but not necessarily) between the father and/or mother and the son or daughter.
- Try to present your characters so that the reader gets an idea of what they are like.

3. Often the best way to study a piece of fiction is to complete an assignment sheet – it helps to focus your mind and remember the important features.

Take the text that you have most recently read in class and complete the following questions. For some of the questions you might have to read the text carefully to work out the answers.

(a) Write down the title of the text, the author, and the year it was published.

....

....

(b) What, in your opinion, is the theme (or themes) of the text?

....

....

(c) How is the story told? First-person narration or third-person narration?

....

....

(d) List the main characters.

....

....

(e) When is the novel/short story/play set?

....

....

(f) Where is it set?

....

....

(g) What is the timescale of the text (the period over which it is set) – years, months, days, hours?

....

....

(h) How is the setting established? Read the beginning carefully to see how the author has established the setting.

....

....

(i) How are the main characters established? How are they introduced?

....

....

(j) What is the relationship between the setting and the characters?

....

....

TOOLS FOR LISTENING AND TALKING

MY PROGRESS

MY LEARNING CHECKLIST

1. *I have explored different types of texts and can give reasons for my personal responses to them.* ◯

2. *I can discuss the structure, setting and characterisation of texts.* ◯

3. *I can identify the main theme or themes of texts.* ◯

4. *I understand what genre and sub-genre mean.* ◯

5. *I have used my knowledge of structure, setting, characterisation and theme to write my own creative texts.* ◯

1. Having explored different genres, I have discovered that the type of books I most enjoy are:

....

....

2. I can find new books to read by visiting the following places:

....

....

FOUR CAPACITIES MIND MAP

1. *I listen to and respect other peoples' opinions on books I have read.*

2. *Reading a range of books helps me to see the world from different viewpoints.*

Reading for enjoyment helps me to become a responsible citizen because:

3. ....

4. ....

5. ....

6. ....

TOOLS FOR LISTENING AND TALKING

GROUP DISCUSSIONS

These four tasks involve working in groups. Before your group does anything, it must appoint a chairperson whose job it is to take charge of the group and ensure that everyone takes his or her turn and that everyone contributes to the discussion.

1. There has been some trouble in your community with teenagers on street corners forming groups about which some older people complain. They say they feel frightened. Your group has been asked to form a committee to present ideas to the local community council to deal with the problem. In your groups, discuss what you think could be done to lessen the problem and make suggestions about introducing the kind of activities that you think might take young people off the streets.

   For this task, try to act like a committee – there won't be one person doing all the talking, jus the chairman keeping control and ensuring that all members, even the quiet ones, get their say. This time you also need someone to take notes which can later be written up and presented as a group report.

2. In your groups, discuss the role of animals in your lives. Think about any pets you have, but also think about the ways in which animals can help human beings – guarding property, helping with search and rescue, and any other roles that you can think of. Also discuss using animals to test medicines and cosmetics – are such uses ever justified? Or is it worth sacrificing a few animals to save human lives? You may also like to discuss environmental issues and what humans can do to save some animals from extinction.

   Again, in this discussion there is no one person presenting a talk – it's a genuine group discussion with everyone volunteering ideas.

. For this talk, each of you should bring to the group a newspaper article that caught your interest. It doesn't have to be long or complex. Each of you in turn will read your article to the rest of the group, who have to take notes on what they hear and then ask questions. Finally, you have to give reasons why you chose the article and say what it is about it that interests you.

It makes sense to choose an article that really interests you or that is about one of your interests – which can be anything, including sport. Take your time as you read the article to give your team members enough time to take in what you are reading and to make notes. Those of you taking notes should listen carefully and make quick notes – you won't have time to write in sentences. You should also be thinking of questions to ask afterwards. You can also say what you think about the article – it may or may not interest you, though, on the other hand, it may kindle an interest that you previously didn't think about.

. Appoint a different chairperson whose job is the same – to make sure that everyone is involved. This time each of you needs to bring to the group a copy of your favourite advert from a newspaper or magazine. Using the advert as a kind of visual aid, you should talk to the group giving your reasons for liking it and saying why you think it is an effective advert.

This time you really want to concentrate not so much on the product as on the way it is advertised.
Does the advert try to create a need that isn't really there?
Does it try to build an image of the type of person who buys the product?
Point out aspects of the advert – the photographs, drawings, language – that appeal to you.

Those of you listening must be prepared to ask questions about the speaker's admiration for the advert and be prepared to say why you also like it – or even why you don't like it.

TOOLS FOR LISTENING AND TALKING

GROUP PRESENTATIONS

In these next tasks, you still work in your discussion groups. The only difference is that for each task you have to elect someone to present the findings of the group to the rest of the class at the end of a given period of time. Your teacher may ask you to give your presentation using presentation software such as PowerPoint; if this is the case, your ICT department may be able to help you lay out and design your slides.

1. In your groups, discuss the role of space exploration. You need to weigh up the benefits of launching another moon mission and even the possibility of a manned mission to Mars. You also need to think about the disadvantages, such as the cost.

   Once you have talked about this subject and reached some conclusions, you then need to plan how you are going to present your findings to the class as a whole. You need to elect one person to make the presentation and decide how the talk is going to be given – should you use a computer projector or a presentation pack such as PowerPoint? You may decide to use cuttings from newspapers or even clips from television.

2. Discuss in your group the role of zoos in our society. Do they serve any functions – educational and environmental – or are they unfair to animals?

   As we increasingly come to respect animals, more and more people are questioning the morality of keeping animals in zoos, yet it cannot be denied that many species would have long ago become extinct if it weren't for zoos.

   Some people think that we should see the zoo from the animals' viewpoint – that they get their amusement by watching these herds of two-legged creatures walk round in a trance-like state gazing at glass and iron bars. Sometimes it is interesting to think of human beings from a totally different viewpoint.

   At the end of the time period, one of the group will present the outcome of your discussions to the rest of the class.

. This time your group is going to make a presentation about the environment. Think about the following questions.

- What measures should we be putting in place now to ensure the survival of the planet?
- Should we start to do without goods that we currently take for granted in order to preserve the earth's resources – or should we leave all that for future generations to worry about?
- Should we start to restrict the use of cars, air travel, and manufactured goods in order to reduce the amount of carbon being pumped into the atmosphere or is the entire environment issue grossly exaggerated?
- Many of the Earth's resources are finite – that means that once they are used up they cannot be replaced. For example, what will happen when there is no longer any oil left? Should we already be planning for that day now? If so, how?

Again, once your group has come to a conclusion one person should present the outcome of your discussions to the rest of the class.

4. Your group is now going to discuss the future of schools.
    - What does your group see as the way forward for the future of school education?
    - Do we have the right mix of subjects?
    - What changes would your group make in order to make schooling more appealing to the majority of young people?
    - Should the whole idea of a school change?
    - What if technology means that we can abolish schools altogether and teach people in their own bedrooms via the computer? Would that work or does school provide an important social side of things where you can meet new people and make friends?
    - Do you think that exams are the most efficient way of testing pupils or can you think of alternatives?

Once you've reached some conclusions, one person should present the group's ideas to the rest of the class.

TOOLS FOR LISTENING AND TALKING

INDIVIDUAL PRESENTATIONS

In these tasks you will make a presentation by yourself, either to a small group or to the whole class. For instance, you might want to consider the use of computer projectors or posters to help make your presentation more interesting. For some of the following presentation ideas, you may want to pull in ideas from other subjects to give a more rounded view of your presentation topic. You also need to be prepared to answer questions about your talk from the people listening to you. Your teacher will tell you how long each talk should be.

1. Prepare a presentation on one of your hobbies or interests. Try to present it in such a way that you explain it clearly (not everyone will necessarily share your interest in birdwatching, after all!) and in an interesting way. Imagine that you are trying to get your classmates to take up your hobby – how would you go about capturing their interest? Again think about how you can use visual aids, including computer projectors, in presenting your hobby. You might also use posters or cut-outs from magazines, as long as they are large enough for everyone to see.

2. Prepare a talk on your most embarrassing moment. This is an opportunity to entertain the class therefore you need to ensure that your talk is properly structured, building up to the climax. You can tell the story in any way you want, but it is probably best to set out the context first of all – where and when was the situation that led to the moment, for example, who was there; what led up to the actual point at which you were consumed with embarrassment; what happened afterwards?

   The saying about jokes is that it isn't the joke that counts, it's the way that you tell them – and that is true of talks. Remember that we all at some time or other in our lives have to deliver a talk. This is your opportunity to practise speaking in public.

3. Whether you are the class technophile (you love technology of all kinds and couldn't live without it) or its greatest technophobe (you hate mobile phones and computers), you must present a talk where you demonstrate how technology affects and influences your lifestyle. The talk can be funny or serious, as long as you engage the interest of your audience. You can, of course, praise technology, which doesn't have to be restricted to mobile phones and iPods. We have seen huge developments in transport of all kinds, including experiments with electric cars and increased public transport. Try to interpret technology in its widest sense.

'ou can also, of course, argue against its development, maintaining that technology has only neant greater slavery for people – we cannot escape mobile phones or computers, which, you :ould argue, rule our lives.

You could also think about the future – will increased technological development do away with the need for school, for example, as we can all – teacher and pupils alike – work from home, contacting each other by computer or video technology. Could it be that we will never have to leave our homes?

. Think about the importance and place of music in your life.

- Do you enjoy listening to music and, if so, what kinds of music do you listen to?
- Can you play a musical instrument? If so, what do you enjoy about it?
- What would life be like without music?

Give a talk about what is important about music for you.

. Prepare a talk on the joy and pressures of being young. Is it all fun with nothing to worry about? No responsibilities? Or are there pressures that adults don't always realise?

It is claimed (and you must have heard it) that your school days are the best days of your life. What that saying means, most probably, is that the best days of your life are when you are young. The trouble is, because you are young and haven't experienced any other kind of days, it's difficult to judge. But when adults make these claims, are they forgetting the pressures of being young? Your talk can explore all the joys and the problems of being twelve or thirteen, just as you start your teenage years. Do you enjoy the freedom of having few responsibilities or do you worry about the future and the time when you will have responsibilities? When you are twelve or thirteen are you really free to enjoy yourself?

TOOLS FOR LISTENING AND TALKING

MY PROGRESS

MY LEARNING CHECKLIST

1. *I have contributed my ideas and opinions to group discussions.* ◯

2. *I have listened carefully to other people's ideas and opinions, and have encouraged others to take part in group discussions.* ◯

3. *I can work with others to prepare a group presentation.* ◯

4. *I can give an individual talk in front of other people, taking into account the audience I am speaking to.* ◯

5. *I can clearly communicate information, ideas and opinions.* ◯

1. Being able to give an individual talk is important in my everyday life because:

....

....

2. In group discussions it is important that:

....

....

FOUR CAPACITIES MIND MAP

1. *Letting me give my opinion clearly.*

2.

3.

4.

5.

6.

Having skills for talking helps to build my confidence by:

ANSWERS

TOOLS FOR WRITING

Quick Questions

1. (a) Edinburgh is the capital city of Scotland.
   (b) Facebook is a networking organisation.
   (c) Spaghetti Bolognese is my favourite Italian meal.
2. father, Harald Dahl, Norwegian, town, Oslo, Sarpsborg, father, grandfather, merchant, store, Sarpsborg, everything, cheese, chicken-wire
3. (a) joy
   (b) trouble / nonsense
   (c) amazement
4. (a) will arrive
   (b) must have
   (c) get, will be, to catch
5. (b) was waiting – past continuous tense
   (c) hadn't seen – past perfect tense
   (d) will be open – future tense
6. (a) beautiful / sapphire / blue
   (b) odd
   (c) empty / yesterday ('shopping centre' is a noun phrase, although 'shopping' does look like an adjective)
   (d) most central / bonnie
7. (a) Michael bought all his tools from the do-it-yourself shop
   (b) The train for Dingwall has been delayed. There are leaves on the line.
   (c) Andrew went to the Odeon in Dunfermline yesterday. He saw the latest blockbuster.

Makes You Think

1. (a) The English language has now reached its millionth word.
   (b) Please fill in all boxes marked with an asterisk.
   (c) You need to enter your address in the space provided.
2. station, floor, grandeur, aristocracy, character, Rebus, sergeant, pictures, notice-board, ones, place, staircase, office, Campbell (Words such as 'it', 'his' and 'He' are pronouns.)
3. (a) rapidity
   (b) idealism
   (c) friendship
4. can call, not, 's, say, asks, isn't, 'm, see, 'm sitting, avoid, 're, want, 've got, 're, don't want, don't like

   It's = it is
   Isn't = is not
   I'm = I am
   They're = They are
   they've = they have
   don't = do not
5. should shake - conditional tense
   is recommended - present continuous
   should be thoroughly dried and aired - conditional tense
6. Pity
   Ugly
   Satisfactory
   Furious
   Silent
7. 'Born March 20th 1977 in Bradford Yorkshire to Mr and Mrs X. We were a family, you know – as happy as most till Dad ran off with a receptionist in 1991, when I was fourteen and at the local comp. This mucked up my school work for quite a while, but that's not why I ended up like this. No. Vincent's to blame for that. Good old Vince. Mum's boyfriend.

Challengers

1. (a) If my grandfather had been alive today he would have been one hundred and sixty-four years old.
   (b) My father would have been one hundred and twenty one.
2. Other ways include:
   By adding '–ation' as in consultation / organisation.
   By adding '–ment' as in merriment / judgement
   By adding '–ity' as in fluidity
   By adding '–ship' as in leadership / authorship
   By adding '-or' as in professor / survivor / actor
   By adding '-er' as in writer / printer / computer
   By adding '-dom' as in wisdom / boredom
   By adding '-hood' as in manhood / knighthood / falsehood
   By adding '-ery' as in slavery
   By adding '-smith' as in wordsmith / goldsmith
   By adding '-ster' as in gangster / mobster / roadster
   By adding '-ful' as in spoonful / helpful
   By adding '-ness' as in quietness / happiness
   By adding '-sion' as in confusion / explosion
   By adding '-ing' as in offering / travelling / listening / speaking
   By adding '-way' as in tramway / railway / roadway / airway
   By adding '-ist' as in canoeist / cyclist
   By adding '-let' as in booklet / pamphlet / ringlet
3. said, have you heard, is let, replied, had not, t is, returned, has, been, told, made, Do, want, has taken, cried, want, have, was ('to know' and 'to tell' are infinitives)
4. is*, is*, makes*, deregulated**, meant**, could be advertised***, had become****
   * present tense
   ** past tense
   ***conditional tense
   ****past perfect tense
5. 'Whoever has opened the window has opened it too wide,' said Miss Brodie. 'Six inches is perfectly adequate. More is vulgar. One should have an innate sense of these things. We ought to be doing history at the moment, according to the timetable. Get out your history books and prop them up in your hands. I shall tell you a little more about Italy. Here is a picture of Dante meeting Beatrice – it is pronounced Beatrichayin Italian which makes the name very beautiful – on the Ponte Vecchio. He fell in love with her at that moment. Mary sit up and don't slouch'.

CREATING TEXTS

Quick Questions

1. Purpose, Structure, Reader, Register

2–4. Your teacher will mark you on how well you have answered these questions

Challengers

1. The answer varies – but it should show your (a) ability to fill in forms, (b) ability to use Internet and various websites, such as Facebook, (c) ability to write reports, (d) ability to write essays, (e) ability to write letters, (f) ability to take notes, (g) ability to express oneself in writing.
2. Many possible answers, but one answer must be to develop reading skills and transfer these to writing skills – also, practice at writing.

ANSWERS

3. Planning helps the writer to structure his or her essay and to keep relevant.

READING FOR UNDERSTANDING

Quick Questions

1. The term 'close reading' means an exercise where there is a piece of text followed by questions which test your understanding of the text and your ability to analyse aspects of a writer's technique.
2. It is important to develop close reading skills in order to increase your ability to follow the ways in which a line of thought are set out and to understand various writer techniques and to be able to incorporate these writer techniques in your own writing.
3. The term 'reading for understanding' means the ability to absorb and comprehend the information presented by a text. For example, so that the reader can follow, say, a set of instructions. Or so that the reader can understand information contained in a label or an advertisement.
4. (a) and (b) Your teacher will mark you on how well you have answered the question
5. Facts can be supported by irrefutable evidence.
6. The answers will be interesting and will include some Scots words. Accept 'haar' which is particular to the East Coast and describes foggy conditions that are also wet.
7. Your teacher will mark you on how well you have answered the question

Makes You Think

1. (a) fact
   (b) fact
   (c) opinion
   (d) opinion
   (e) fact
   (f) fact
   (g) opinion
   (h) opinion

Be Active

1. (a) The narrator goes back to school after 'dinner-time', therefore it must be at midday.
   (b) He enjoyed dinner-time especially when it involved rice pudding and when it was eaten by the 'blazing fire' by the 'white-washed hearth'.
   (c) Any references to 'the blazing fire', 'feet up on the sparkling brass fender', sitting by the fire 'made going back to school even harder', 'I would sit by my fire in my slippers' and the contrast between the 'blazing fire' inside and the 'glum blasts of the foghorn' outside and/or the 'wailing sirens of fogbound ships'.
   (d) Accept either possibility, as long as it is based on a reference. The most likely answer is 'unhappy', because there are many references in the last sentence that suggest his reluctance to go outside, though the expression 'I would scramble into my coat' may suggest an urgency to get back to school.
   (e) Clearly a seaside town – there are many references to the sea and boats.

READING FOR ENJOYMENT

Quick Questions

1. What is the text (novel, play, poem, film, soap) about?
   What techniques have been used to tell us what it's about?

How do those techniques contribute to what it's about?

2. Textual analysis is about the analysis of the way in which a writer has put together a text and the ways in which he or she conveys feelings or emotions. In the case of plays, novels, poems, and film and tv drama, textual analysis is examining the many techniques by which an author portrays his or her theme. It involves the examination of writer technique.
3. Genre means drama, prose, poetry. Sub-genre is the classification within a genre. Each genre canbe further classified or sub-divided. For example, Prose can be sub-divided into Prose Fiction (which includes novels and short stories) and Prose Non-fiction (which includes newspapers articles, essays, biographies, autobiographies, travel books).
   Within Prose Fiction we can further sub-divide novels into crime, horror, science fiction and so on. It's the same with films, where sub-genre can include mystery, westerns, sci-fi, film noire, fantasy.
4. (a) drama – tragedy
   (b) fiction – romance
   (c) fiction – vampire romance (and film – vampire romance)
   (d) film – sci-fi
   (e) tv drama – soap opera
   (f) fiction – disaffected youth
   (g) fiction – fantasy
   (h) fiction – adventure
   (i) tv news – non-fiction
   (j) poetry – narrative poem

Makes You Think

1. (a) The way in which a story has been put together using time.
2. Advantages of First Person Narration
   The reader gets to know and usually like the narrator, and weget to know exactly what he / she is thinking because we are 'inside the narrator's head'. Everything is told from his or her point of view.
   Disadvantages of First Person Narration
   The narrator has to be present at all times or else he/she has to learn of important events from other people – often by a conversation that employs flashback – or from a newspaper, a telephone call, a text, or an email. The reader has to accept the narrator's word for everything.
3. There are various *p*. The two most common are first person narrator and third person narrator.

Challengers

1–3. Your teacher will mark your answer on how well you have answered the question.

Make the Link

Jonathan Harker's Journal

a) (1) The Carpathians are in Eastern Europe and stretch from the Czech Republic in the northwest to Poland, Hungary, Ukraine and Romania in the east, to Serbia in the south.
   (2) Transylvania is in the west of Romania.
   (3) The Danube is the second longest river in Europe and it flows into the Black Sea.
   (4) Budapest.
   (5) An Ordnance survey maps are the maps produced by Britain's national mapping agency. Ordnance refers to weaponry and the military. The maps were first produced in the Eighteenth

Century for the military, initially to provide maps of strategic importance for dealing with rebellions in the Highlands of Scotland and the wars with France.

b) (1) Paprika is a spice.
(2) Paprika comes from Hungary / Serbia.
(3) A chicken stew with paprika.
(4) Any recipe that includes paprika as an ingredient.

c) (1) The narrator uses 'I'.
(2) A journal is a diary, kept daily, especially of travels or events, usually meant for public readership. A personal journal is called a diary.
(3) He wants to get the recipe for her – therefore he must know her quite well. If he is getting a recipe for her, it may mean that he wants her to cook for him.
(4) Your teacher will mark your answer on how well you have answered the question.